First Printing, 2021

# A Question From Baby

Beth Custer

I can't wait to
know you! For a
life of happiness,
I'll strive!

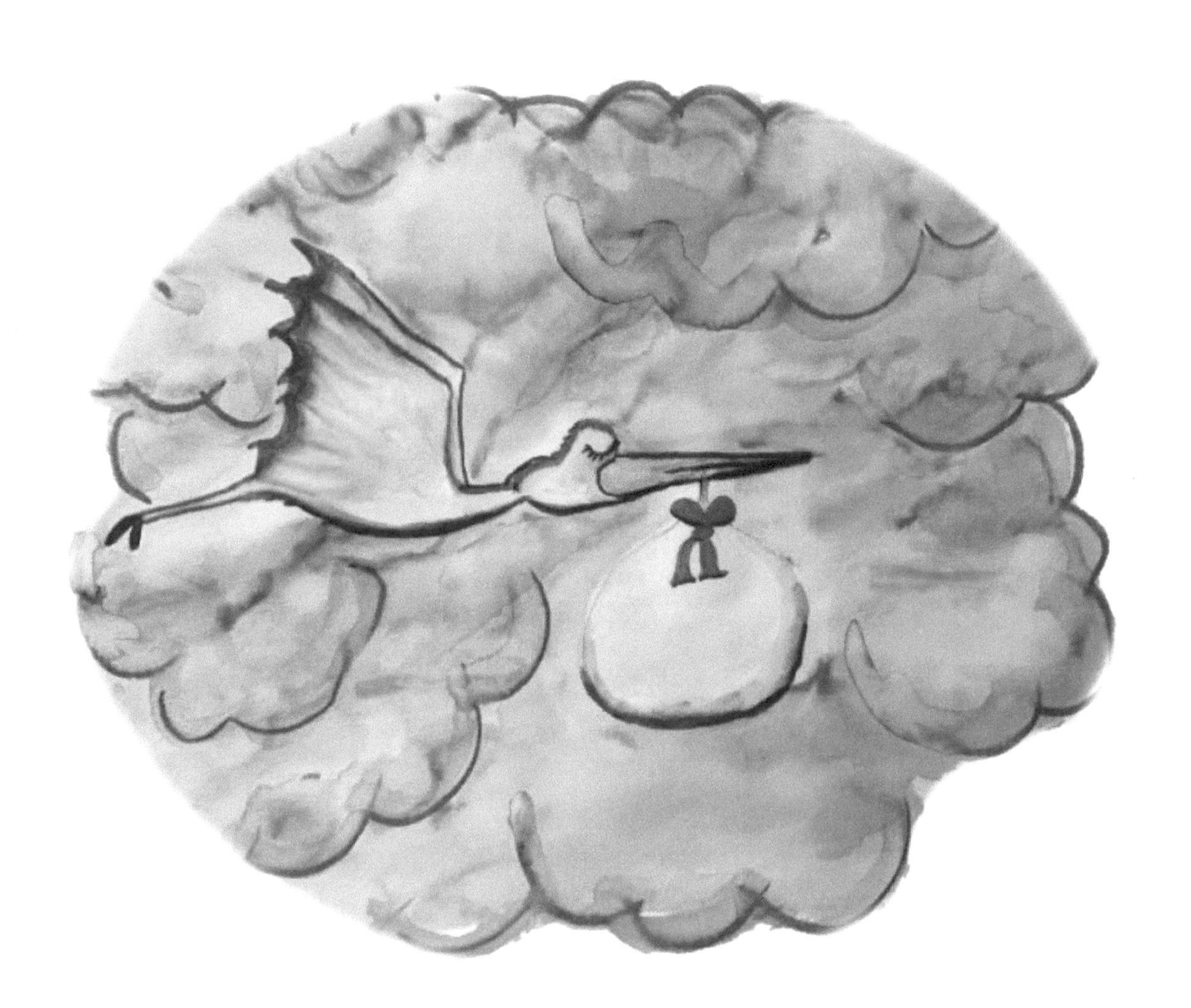

In a household full of love, I know that I will thrive!

But there's room
for more love in
this world I'll
learn to know.

And there is no
one else whom I'd
love to help me
grow.

You are already
so important- this
is quite apparent!

What I want to ask is…

Will you please by my Godparent?

This book is dedicated to all loving parents and Godparents.

Lightning Source UK Ltd.
Milton Keynes UK
UKHW051406010821
388016UK00002B/22